BLOOD
AND
FIRE

Religious and Moral Education Press
An imprint of Chansitor Publications Ltd,
a wholly owned subsidiary of Hymns Ancient & Modern Ltd
St Mary's Works, St Mary's Plain
Norwich, Norfolk NR3 3BH

First published 1996

ISBN 1 85175-108-4

Note
Information on how this book can be used in schools is provided on pages 90 to 92.

Designed and typeset by Topics – The Creative Partnership, Exeter

Illustrations by Clive Wakfer

Printed in Great Britain by BPC Wheatons Ltd, Exeter
for Chansitor Publications Ltd, Norwich

BLOOD
AND
FIRE

TERENCE COPLEY

ACKNOWLEDGEMENTS

The origins of the Salvation Army are still quite near to us in time, for it was born during the lifetimes of our great-grandparents or great-great-grandparents. The Army takes the same view that it did in its earliest days: that if people won't come to the Church, the Church should come to the people. I used to walk past the York Citadel, which has a foundation stone laid by Elijah Cadman not much more than a hundred years ago. This one-time chimney sweep, one-time professional boxer rose to be a great champion of the Salvation Army. But my first-hand knowledge and understanding of the Army comes from the writings of Frederick and John Coutts, to the officers who contributed to the little book *This Is My Call*, and to the Army newspapers and magazines *Values*, *Salvationists*, *Young Soldier* and of course *The War Cry*.

People brought the books to life: Captain and Mrs Captain Johnson at the Belper Corps (Derbyshire) and Captain Laurie Brown, who together with Mrs Captain Evangeline Brown was an officer of the Exeter Temple Corps at the time of the writing of this book. His personal insights and advice on those puzzling aspects of the Army such as the distinction between Mrs Captain Smith and Captain Mrs Smith were enormously helpful to me as an outsider looking in.

RMEP are beginning to get as used to their association with crime literature as I am to membership of the Crime Writers' Association. Mary Mears as editor has in each book in the series brought to bear her talent not only for imaginative suggestion but also for spotting the mistakes in plotting that get past the writer. She is a Moriarty among editors.

The good-heartedness of all the Salvationists I met was a long way from the fictitious crime in these pages, but Salvationists have never been strangers to the idea of fighting sin. William Booth's *In Darkest England and the Way Out* (1890) is still a landmark as a mixture of vision, practical proposal and the then new awareness that the 'vice' or sin of individuals thrives more easily in appalling social conditions and that the problems of society and those of individuals need to be tackled together.

The other books in this Mysteries Series have each carried cryptic clues, even in the Acknowledgements. Perhaps I should therefore conclude that if I were ever to fire a volley, 1 Thessalonians 5:4 might come in useful. Salvationist readers will solve that one immediately!

T.C.

About You

In this book, you, the reader, play the role of one of the detectives in the Quicksolve Detective Agency.

The Quicksolve team were thrilled with their earlier successes in the cases of *Sudden Death at the Vicarage*, *The Stolen Statue*, *The Writing on the Wall* and *The Missing Minister*. They have established a reputation for solving crimes with some sort of religious link. Imagine you are in the office enjoying a drink and a chat with some of the others about the clues in these cases – that silent suspicious housekeeper at the vicarage, the way the writing on the synagogue wall looked so professional and the astonishing way in which the larger-than-life-size statue vanished.

You're talking in a rather loud voice about the important part you played in solving these mysteries when you notice that the room has gone silent around you. You're delighted to be so successful as a story-teller and continue to inform everyone how well you did in those earlier cases. You ask loudly just where the Boss would be without you. The whole firm just about depends on you! A polite cough behind causes you to turn and see with horror not a dead body, not an armed intruder, not an escaped zoo animal, but the Boss. He's not looking very pleased at your performance.

'I see you're not doing much at the moment,' says the Boss, menacingly.

'Er, yes, I can, er, spare a minute or two.'

'Then come into my office at once.'

'Oh dear.'

You follow the Boss into his office. To your relief, the two of you are not alone. Two other people are already in the room. One is a black female in her twenties, dressed in a black skirt, black leather jacket, black tights and black shoes. The other is a man in his forties, dressed in a grey suit, grey socks, grey shoes. Even the handkerchief in his top pocket looks grey from where you're sitting. He needs a shave, so his face has a grey beard shadow. The Boss seems slightly nervous of this strange couple, so you suppose they must be very rich clients of your detective agency.

'This is Miss, er, Mrs, er, Ms, er, I didn't quite catch your name,' says the Boss to the woman.

'No name,' she replies.

'Er, yes, exactly. Ms Noname. And this is Mr, er, Mr, er, ...,' he falters again.

'Ditto,' says the grey man.

'Ah yes,' says the Boss, 'Mr Ditto. Well, I'll leave you three together then.' With a sigh of relief, the Boss almost runs to the door and disappears.

No sooner is the door closed than the mysterious pair get up and walk around, ignoring you altogether. They open the door to check no-one is listening outside, they open the drawers in the Boss's desk and filing-cabinet – presumably to look for hidden microphones.

'All clear,' says Ms Noname.

'All clear,' Ditto replies. They sit down again, facing you.

'We are here on a matter of possible state security,' the woman begins, lowering her voice almost to a whisper, 'an attempted assassination of Lord, Lord

Ca*** .' You aren't clear whether she is saying 'Carntsey'
or 'can't say'.

'With your help it can be prevented,' adds the man.

'Surely,' you venture, 'this ought to be a matter for
Special Branch or Military Intelligence, not a private

detective agency.' Ms Noname looks at you as if you're a complete idiot.

'We *are* Special Branch,' she answers. 'Interpol have put us on to this.'

'Mmm. Special,' adds Mr Ditto, pausing to pick some grey fluff from his sleeve.

'I really don't think Quicksolve can add anything to your expertise,' you begin to reply modestly. You almost wish the Boss would come back and help you deal with this strange couple.

'That's where you're wrong,' says Ms Noname. 'You're famous for your work with religious groups. You've been commended.'

'And recommended,' Ditto again.

'People in high places know your work,' Ms Noname adds mysteriously.

'You mean mountaineers and airline pilots?' you can't resist quipping. This time they look at each other then back at you, ignoring your attempt at a joke altogether.

'Besides,' continues Ms Noname, 'we've had a lot of staff cuts lately, to save money. So we have to buy in outside people to help us, especially on crime prevention. That's what this is all about – unless you fail and they kill him.' You ignore the chilling feeling her last words create.

'Which religious group is involved in this case?' you ask.

'The Salvation Army.'

'Oh, yes,' you speak confidently and try to look expert, but all you can vaguely remember about them is that they wear uniforms and often have services in the street with a brass band to play the music.

'They've been infiltrated,' Mr Ditto explains.

'We want you to find out who the inside agent is. Our intelligence reports tell us that a top hit man – or woman – has been sent to infiltrate the Salvation Army and kill the target.'

4

'Why would anyone want to infiltrate the Salvation Army? What's it got to do with assassination plots?'

'That's easy. One of the top Salvation Army bands is performing in front of Lord Ca*** ,' Ms Noname coughs, so you're still not sure of the name. 'The concert is at one of the big Salvationist meeting-halls tomorrow. Our information suggests that they're going to disguise the killer as a member of the Salvation Army band. He – or she – may have a bomb. Or a gun. Or something else. We don't know who he – or she – is.'

'Why don't you just cancel the concert or tell His Lordship to stay at home?'

'Because they'll simply try again when we're not expecting them. In that case they'll be much more likely to succeed. Better to catch the killer in the act and break up the gang. That way it can't happen later somewhere else.'

'Welcome to the case,' says Ditto. To your surprise they both stand up and start to head for the door.

'Wait a minute! I don't even know whether you are who you say you are.'

'We don't carry identity cards – what if we left them on the bus or in a shop? In any case, how would you recognize a Special Branch card if you saw one?' adds Ms Noname. You finger your own Quicksolve identity card in your pocket thoughtfully. Is their explanation good enough?

'What have I got to find out?' you ask.

'Give us the name of the killer, the motive and the method before the murder can happen. That's all. We'll do the rest.'

'That's *all*?'

'Not quite all. We're off now to attend to a much bigger case, but if you want to contact us, you can ring this number.' Ms Noname gives you a card with a phone number on it. Before you can ask any more questions they've gone.

How You Play Detective

In this investigation you will need to work out:

- who is the killer,
- the motive or reason for the assassination attempt,
- the method the killer is planning to use.

If you can find all three correctly, you will have solved the case.

Every few pages in this book, you are asked to choose what you, the detective, do next. When you have decided which clue to follow up or what action to take, you go to another page and read on. But, as in real-life detection, you are working against time. There are several ways of reaching the correct solution to the case, but some take longer than others. Sometimes you will have to decide whether to spend time on extra clues, or whether to manage without. Some choices take longer and tell you in advance to 'add 1 hour to your time score'. When you turn to some other pages, you may find that a choice you have made loses you an hour or more when you weren't expecting it to. This too is like real life because some things take longer than we expect – but the hour(s) must be added to your time score. It is important to write down all these extra hours so that you can keep track of your time score. They are not real hours that you have to add on to reach the solution!

Your time score starts at zero at the beginning of the case. At the very end of the book you will work out a final score based on how much of the solution you got right as well as how long it took you, i.e. the size of your time score. If you use extra clues that add to your time spent, you may be much more likely to get the right solution. If you don't use them, you will be going for a quicker solution, but your chances of getting it wrong may be much higher. It's up to you to weigh up the risks!

You will need a pen or pencil and paper for keeping a note of your time score. It might be useful to have a pad handy to jot down names of suspects, or details of the case. As you near the end of the book, you may want to write down your deductions – or guesses – about the solution before you actually go on to check it. It's also a good idea to have something you can use as a bookmark so that you don't lose your place, especially if you have to jump to another page to read a clue then back again to where you came from.

Now read on. Good luck with the case! Quicksolve are relying on you.

You begin your investigation

The Boss has evidently put you in charge of this case, but where do you start when you know so little?

Choose:

- Whether to find out some basic facts about the Salvation Army before you start the case. To do this, go to page 10.

- Whether to ring the telephone number you've been given by your two mystery visitors and demand to know more. To do this, go to page 9.

- Whether to find out more about Lord Carntsey (if that's his real name) by looking him up in *Who's Who*. To do this, go to page 22.

You check out 'corps' in a dictionary

You find that your assistant is enthusiastic, but wrong. 'Corps' really does mean a body, but it means a body of people acting together. The word is commonly used to refer to a unit in an army acting under military command. 'Corps' and 'corpse' come from the same Latin word, *corpus*, but have quite different meanings in English. A local group of Salvation Army members are called a corps because they are part of an army, not because of a dead body! Your assistant has set you off on a false clue, but fortunately it hasn't taken up any extra time.

Make your next choice quickly:

- You could ring the Ecclesfield Corps & Community Centre, by going to page 12.

- You could find out more about Lord Carntsey, by going to page 22 to look him up in *Who's Who*.

You ring the number your two mystery visitors gave you

It's the number of a mobile phone, so they might have the phone with them in a pocket or bag. But it rings ... and rings ... and rings. No-one answers. You notice that the Boss has come into the room and is watching you.

'I'm just trying to find out more from our clients,' you explain. 'They really gave me very little information to start from.'

'Don't waste time doing that,' says the Boss, crossly. 'That's like asking them to solve the case for you. Get on with it yourself. That's what they're paying us for.'

Choose:

- Either to go to page 10 to find out some basic facts about the Salvation Army.
- Or to go to page 22 to find out more about Lord Carntsey by looking him up in *Who's Who*.

You find out some basic facts about the Salvation Army

You start with the encyclopedia on your desk. From this you learn that the Salvation Army is a Christian organization founded by William Booth, who was its first leader or General. Its members wear uniform, and their street marches and open-air services with brass bands and their flag are well known. The Salvation Army started in England in the 1860s. It now works in over eighty countries and more than a hundred languages.

Salvationists are famous world wide for their welfare work among distressed and 'down and out' people, including alcoholics, those sleeping rough and drug addicts. Many towns have a Salvation Army 'Clothing Bank' in a car-park, where clothes that might be of use to some of their homeless clients can be left.

The Salvation Army also runs a Family Tracing Service to help people contact close relatives they've lost touch with through family breakdown or quarrels.

That's a beginning, but it still doesn't give you much to go on. You wonder why they're called an army. And why 'Salvation'? The dictionary on your desk tells you that 'salvation' means deliverance from sin, from missing the mark, getting it wrong with God. It also means freedom, being saved from danger or difficulty or destruction.

You wonder whether there's a Salvation Army place of worship near you. How can you find out? Your assistant has arrived and suggests you start with the telephone directory.

'The telephone directory?' you reply. 'Churches don't have telephones.' Your assistant persists in looking under S, however, and grinning at proving you wrong, passes you the directory.

10

There's a boxed list of numbers next to a badge and the motto 'With heart to God and hand to man'. First the number and address for the UK headquarters are listed. After that comes the number and address for the Divisional Commander for your area – just like an army – and then a list of places near you called Local Corps & Community Centres.

Your assistant points excitedly at the list: 'That's got to be a clue. It says "Local Corpse". There's already a dead body. They've missed the "e" off the end of "corpse". There's a big crime going on somewhere. Let's check it out fast. We're definitely on to something here.'

You must choose:

- Whether to check out 'corps' in a dictionary, by going to page 8.

- Whether to ring the branch of the Salvation Army nearest you, the Ecclesfield Local Corps & Community Centre, and see if you can visit them, by going to page 12.

- Whether to find out more about Lord Carntsey by going to page 22 to look him up in *Who's Who.*

You ring the Ecclesfield Local Corps & Community Centre

Although it's a weekday morning and not Sunday, the person who answers the telephone, a Mrs Captain Diane Jones, says that the citadel, as she calls it, is open for a coffee morning. You're welcome to drop in and she will meet you there. Your assistant eagerly looks up 'citadel' in the dictionary and finds that it means fort or stronghold. Another army word. You wonder why Diane Jones is Mrs Captain Diane Jones and what that means.

From the outside the citadel doesn't look like a church: it's more like a hall or small cinema. You go inside, passing through the entrance porch and into a rather plain hall. There are benches placed in rows and a raised platform with seats and music stands as if a band might sit there. At the front you notice the Salvation Army flag and a bench facing the hall with JESUS SAVES painted on it. A large version of the Salvation Army badge has been painted on the wall facing you.

In one corner, stacking tables have been put up and a jumble sale is in full swing. Thirty or forty people must be busy buying. Some of the people serving at the stalls are in ordinary clothes and some are in uniform. Eventually you are spotted by a woman in uniform who gives you a wave and a smile and hurries over. She introduces herself as Mrs Captain Diane Jones, the person you spoke to on the phone. She is joined by a young woman of about eighteen not in uniform who she introduces as her daughter Elizabeth. A cup of coffee appears in your hand and you find yourself eating a tasty piece of homemade cake with it – and then giving a donation towards the fund.

'It's for the Army this week,' Diane Jones explains, 'clothes for the needy, blankets, food, that sort of thing.'

'The British Army? Surely the government supplies them with what they need?'

'No, no! The Sally Army. Sally Anns!'

'Sally Anns?'

'Just one of our nicknames,' she explains. 'Look, I'm a bit busy this morning but Lizzie's home from university on vac. She'll show you round and answer any questions you've got. Just ask. Bye. God bless!' She shakes your hand and bustles off into the coffee crowd. You sit down next to Lizzie on one of the benches.

'I'm finding all this a bit confusing,' you admit, 'all the army talk.'

'Oh that,' she grins. 'It's a bit puzzling to outsiders, but you see William Booth, our founder, believed that the Devil is real. He's not a cartoon figure with horns and a spear and a red tail, but a real Evil Power, out to get people, to harm, to destroy. When you look around the world, you've got to admit,' she grins again, 'he's remarkably good at his job. Wars, famines, drugs, crime, alcohol abuse, unhappiness, wrecked lives. All this in a planet where there's enough food for everyone and people could live in peace and happiness! So the Devil, or Evil if you prefer to call it that, is doing very well.

'William Booth believed the only way a power like that can be fought is by discipline, by organization, by people working together with the inspiration and example of Jesus. We must be organized and effective like an army. That's why we use army language. The citadel – the fort – is the church building, and the corps – the fighting unit – is the people.

'Booth used everyday language rather than "churchy" language for lots of other things:

14

"meetings" instead of "services", for example. Instead of hymns played on the organ, he used popular tunes played by bands, which people linked with everyday entertainment in those days, like pop music to us. His meetings had a friendly informal style instead of following the words of a service from a book.

'In Booth's day, poor people didn't feel very welcome in many churches because there were rented seats and the poor people had to sit in the free seats. Imagine how they felt. The free seats had a notice on so that you could find them. Sitting in one was like wearing a label in public saying that you were poor. But in our meetings all the seats were always free ...'

Lizzie carries on talking, but you stop listening. Coming down the hall towards you is your assistant, walking slowly, white enough to have seen a ghost, and clutching a piece of paper. It's a fax which has just arrived at the office for you.

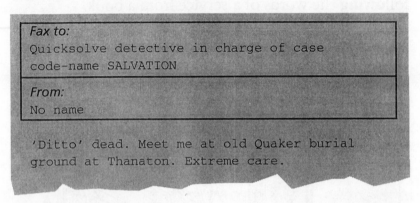

Fax to:
Quicksolve detective in charge of case
code-name SALVATION

From:
No name

'Ditto' dead. Meet me at old Quaker burial ground at Thanaton. Extreme care.

The babble of the jumble sale and coffee morning in the background washes over you as you think about that man in grey who was in your office not long ago. Poor Ditto. He'll never be the same again.

Now you must decide:

- Whether to go to the old Quaker burial ground at Thanaton, by turning to page 24.
- Whether to spend an hour here with Lizzie and find out a lot more about the Salvation Army, by going to page 17. This might help to prepare you properly for what you're heading into. If you decide to stay here with Lizzie, you will have to **add 1 hour to your time score**.

You spend an hour with Lizzie

Add 1 hour to your time score.

'Let's start with the badge,' she begins, 'It does what any badge does – tells outsiders who we are and reminds us of what we believe.' She takes you to where you can see the badge painted on the wall at the front of the hall.

'The motto "Blood and Fire" stands for the blood of Jesus and the fire of the Holy Spirit. We believe God's Holy Spirit sets people on fire to preach and to live out God's love for them. Fire cleans things as well. It can burn away impurities. So it reminds us of our belief

that the Holy Spirit can make you clean. The colour blue stands for the purity of God (think of clear blue sea or sky!), yellow is the fire of the Holy Spirit and red ...'

'The blood of Jesus?' you interrupt, trying to show you've learned something.

'Full marks,' she laughs. 'Then in the crest there's the Cross. This represents the cross Jesus died on, but it's empty now because we believe he's risen. The "S" stands for ...'

'Salvation?' you try again.

'Good! Any ideas about the crown?' This time you're stuck.

'It's the crown of life – life after death – for the Christian. The crossed swords? Try again.'

'Battle?'

'Yes. It's the fight for God, not a war between national armies, but the battle against Evil. The sun

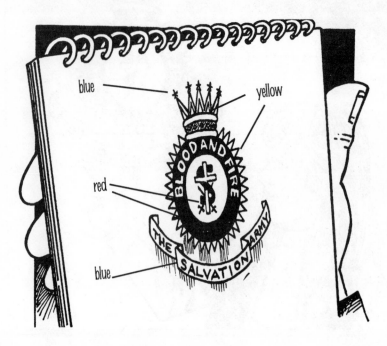

represents the light and fire of the Holy Spirit. So our badge is full of meaning.'

'But what about generals and lieutenants and all that?'

'Well, the officers are the full-time workers, like clergy in other Christian churches or rabbis for Jews. The other members are known as soldiers. If you're called to be an officer you go to the William Booth Memorial College at Denmark Hill in London for two years as an officer cadet. There you study and prepare for life in the Army as a full-time worker. Then you're commissioned – another word borrowed from the military. You come out of college as a lieutenant and your training continues on the job. By then you're in charge of a corps or, less often, a social-services centre.'

'Help for the homeless? Helping people kick drugs?'

'Yes, that sort of thing. But if you run a local corps you're still helping people who have problems. It may be the death of a close friend or relative or a personal problem or illness – anything, or anyone! We don't just look after our own people who belong to the Army.

'After five years as a lieutenant,' she continues, 'you become a captain and after fifteen years as a captain you become a major. Promotions above that are not automatic. The higher ranks are colonel, commissioner and so on.'

'The top rank is general?'

'Yes. There's only one general for the Salvation Army in the world.'

'William Booth was the first?'

'That's right.'

'The General could be a woman?'

'Of course.'

'And everyone has to obey the General?'

'Not quite! The General's not a dictator, but at the same time the Army is led from the top. Officers are "posted" – sent to places to work – like the ordinary army. They get a letter containing marching orders and farewell orders. It tells them about six weeks before a move where they're going.'

'Six weeks isn't really very long. Can they be sent anywhere?'

'In theory, but the needs of their family, especially children at school, are taken into account.'

'It must be very hard on their wives.'

'Or husbands. We have women officers – in fact two thirds of the officers in the UK are women. Officers must marry an officer, if they do marry, and you can see why. It means they both share the same faith and outlook, and they can be moved to a posting together and at quite short notice.'

'So that's what Mrs Captain Jones means?'

'Yes.'

'But all this army language – officers, postings, marching orders?'

'There's lots more. When Salvationists die we say that they've been "promoted to glory". You might say "gone to heaven", but we believe it really will be a glorious existence, even though we don't know in any detail what it'll be like. When we join the Army we sign the Articles of War – that's a statement of Army beliefs to show what we're signing up for. Remember, soldiers in national armies have to sign up when they enrol. "Firing a cartridge" is another phrase used in the Salvation Army, but it means giving money, not shooting someone!'

'But why use all this army language?'

'Several reasons: William Booth believed that people needed to fight the Devil by joining together in an organized way like an army. The language came naturally to him, though the Salvation Army only got its present name in 1878. It had other names before then: Christian Mission, Hallelujah Army, Volunteer Army ...'

'I like the sound of "Volunteer". It's more friendly. After all, you're not forced to join. You are really volunteers.'

'Yes, but in another way we're not. We feel God has called us, and when God calls,' she laughs, 'you fall into line and obey the orders. We're all full-time Christians even if we're not full-time officers. In the Sally Army everybody counts, not just the officers. All the soldiers go along on Sundays and on mid-week evenings to help in all the services and activities of the corps.'

'Mmm. You spoke of several reasons for the army language?'

'It's used in the Bible. Paul was a famous Christian in the early days after Jesus and he talks about "fighting the good fight", being a "good soldier of Christ", putting on "the whole armour of God". He lists this armour: the belt of truth, the body armour of righteousness, the shield of faith, the helmet of salvation and the sword of the Spirit.'

Lizzie pauses to draw breath, then giggles. 'I've given you quite a lecture, haven't I? I hope it's helped.'

There's so much more you might need to know, and so little time. Your hour is almost spent.

Now you have to choose:

- Whether to go to the rendezvous at the old Quaker burial ground at Thanaton, if you haven't been there yet, by turning to page 24.

- Whether to try to find out more about Ms Noname and Mr Ditto, your strange clients who wouldn't even give you their real names. Perhaps a friend of yours who's a police constable can help you. You can drive down to see him by turning to page 32.

You look up Lord Carntsey in *Who's Who*

Who's Who is a guide-book to titled, well-known or distinguished (living) people. So it should tell you who this man you're supposed to be rescuing from an assassination attempt is. You ring your local library and ask a librarian you know to look up Lord Carntsey. Yes, he is listed. Yes, your acquaintance will jot down the main facts in the entry straight away. These notes are soon sliding out of the fax machine in your office:

ECCLESFIELD LIBRARY   10.45AM

Carntsey, Albert, Life Peer, industrialist.

He's a very wealthy industrialist who was born in the West Midlands.

He made his first million in nail-manufacturing then branched out into a special form of glue. This glue bonds surfaces without nails being needed. It makes Superglue look easy to separate!

Hobbies: active interest in Salvation Army including fund-raising and work with homeless people, e.g. soup runs.

You pause in your reading. You can feel warm breath on your neck. Someone is standing right behind you. It's your assistant.

'I wonder if he runs faster than the soup?'

'Soup runs deliver soup to people living rough on the streets, you idiot! In London they serve two thousand people on each nightly soup run at a cost of about £600. It's all that keeps some people alive in the coldest nights of the winter.'

'How do you know all that?' asks your assistant. You decide to leave your assistant marvelling at your

22

brilliance, so you carefully cover the open encylopedia on your desk by putting the dictionary on top.

'So the target of the attack is a wealthy industrialist who is actively involved in helping the Sally Army?'

'That's about it.'

'Is he a member of the Salvation Army, then?'

'Apparently not – it just says 'active interest'. I don't suppose he wears the uniform and all that.'

- If you haven't contacted the branch of the Salvation Army nearest you, you must ring the Ecclesfield Local Corps & Community Centre and see if you can visit them, by going to page 12.

- If you have already visited this Salvation Army citadel, try to meet Lord Carntsey and find out more about him, by going to page 34.

You go to the old Quaker burial ground at Thanaton

Thanks to the map-reading skills of your assistant, it takes you about an hour to drive five kilometres and find this old Quaker burial ground.

Add 1 hour to your time score.

As you arrive, your assistant makes a joke about the burial ground being for old Quakers, so where do they put the young ones? You just groan loudly.

You expected to find the burial ground crawling with police, photographers, forensic scientists, fingerprint experts, medical experts and special constables to keep the press and public away. To your surprise, there are only two cars parked there, and they're both empty. You wonder if you are, after all, at the right place. Rather gingerly you park and get out of your car. Your assistant makes the excuse of being tied up unknotting a shoe and stays behind, so you are left to enter the burial ground alone.

There's a low stone wall with a rusty metal gate that creaks then bangs shut behind you. You might as well have blown a bugle, so much for trying to keep your arrival quiet! It's clear that the burial ground has not been used for many years. Weeds are everywhere and creepers have grown into the wall. But it's peaceful rather than spooky. There are no stone slabs on the grassy mounds, just rows of small, almost identical marker stones with inscriptions stating only the person's name and dates of birth and death. You read the one nearest to you. It's absolutely plain. No decoration, just a plain stone.

24

It starts to rain. Ditto is dead. Perhaps the murderer is lurking here somewhere. Perhaps you've been lured into a trap. You realize you're in a very grave situation. Where is the mysterious Ms Noname and where is the body? You're in a burial ground, but you can't see a corpse! The small marker stones are only about 60 cm high, not tall or wide enough for a person to hide behind. Where can the others be?

Suddenly you freeze. You can hear a deathly noise: 'Cooooeeee, – Cooooeeee ... ' Then there's a shriek – 'Aaaargh!' – and a crash – 'Crump!' It's

coming from behind you. Quickly you swing round to face your hideous attacker. Whew! It's only your assistant, who has been running to catch you up, tripped and fallen headlong across the wet grass, skidding along head first. A marker stone acts as a brake, and halts your assistant's skid with another 'Crump' and a slightly flatter head. You hurry over, and crouch down to lift your muddy assistant up off the slippery grass.

As you reach your full height you're aware that someone else is right behind you, standing so close to you that your back is touching their front. You jump forward with shock, and drop your dazed assistant back onto the muddy grass again as you spin round. It's Ms Noname, still dressed completely in black, this time with a black raincoat.

'Ssh,' she says, putting a finger to her lips, 'there's no time to lose. We'll send your assistant back to Quicksolve in your car. You must come with me immediately.' Taking your arm she starts to walk you quickly towards the gate. You look back at the empty burial ground again.

'But the police? They aren't here ...'

'We don't bother with the local police. Now hurry!' She starts to run, pulling you along with her. Your assistant's sitting puzzled on the ground back where you were.

'Where are we going?' you ask.

'To my car.'

'But where?'

'Stop asking questions! You'll see.'

You arrive at one of the parked cars. Ms Noname unlocks the passenger door and almost pushes you into the seat, shutting the door on you. She hurries across to leave a note for your assistant on the windscreen of your car.

Think for a moment! Has Ditto even been here, or

could this be a plot to kidnap you? Do you know he's dead? Could she have killed him? Whose side is she on?

You've only seconds to decide what to do next:

• You could jump out of Ms Noname's car while she's getting in, run to your own car and drive off. If you haven't already done so, you could then spend an hour with Lizzie Jones to find out more about the Salvation Army so that you're more clued up on this weird case. To do this, go to page 17.

• You could escape in your own car and visit a friend of yours who's a police constable to try to find out more about Ms Noname. To do this, go to page 32.

• You could risk staying with Ms Noname and letting her drive you – to where? To do this, go to page 28.

If you decide to escape, remember to phone Quicksolve and ask someone to rescue your assistant.

You risk staying in the car with Ms Noname

Your mysterious surviving client hurries back and gets into the driver's seat. She then tests the car advert '0 to 60 in 5 seconds' by performing an accelerator-down, roar-away start, with tyres screeching, gravel flying and water from the puddles splashing everywhere. Your assistant, who has just come through the gate to see what's happening, is drenched as you hurtle past.

For you it's now a white-knuckle ride. It reminds you of theme-park visits you made in your childhood. You remember the roar of the ride and that feeling you used to get at the moment when it was too late to get off. The same sensation comes to you now. You are heading down the country lanes at the sort of speed that makes the view through the windscreen look like a fast-moving arcade or video game. Bends, narrow roads, humpback bridges – all flash past without any reduction of speed. Your client seems quite relaxed about it, however.

'Er, I didn't see Mr Ditto back there,' you venture, making sure your seat belt's securely fastened. Ms Noname tosses her head as if to indicate something behind you. You look around cautiously, half fearing what you're going to see. On the back seat there are two grey shoes, a pair of grey socks and a grey suit neatly folded, but no body. Are these his clothes? Is he really dead? Or is this some sort of attempt to fool you?

'Where are we going now?' you ask.

'How's your side of the enquiry going?' she asks you in reply, ignoring your question completely.

'Well,' you try to sound optimistic, 'I'm making progress on the Salvation Army background, but I can't

28

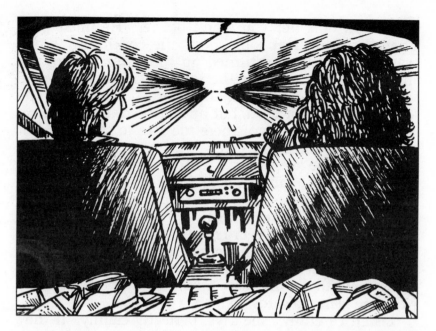

say I've got very far yet. How's your side of the enquiry going?'

'This has created a problem or two,' she nods towards the rear again as if Ditto is the biggest nuisance in the world, 'but Ditto was still alive when I reached him and he managed to give me a clue.'

'A clue? You didn't mention that before. What did he say?'

'He kept muttering one phrase over and over again.'

'What was that?' you ask breathlessly.

'School dinner.'

'*School dinner?*'

'Mmm. Ditto kept repeating it.'

'You mean school dinner made him burp?'

'Nah! He just kept mumbling it, over and over again. "School dinner, school dinner".'

'Was he poisoned, then?'

'Shot at close range. Want to see for yourself?' She nods towards the rear as if he might be in the boot.

Your look tells her you won't bother. 'He must have gone there to meet somebody,' she continues, 'but it was a trap. Whoever turned up shot him. I think it's more than likely it was the same hit man or woman who's going to try to kill Lord Carntsey. Anyway, the killer left Ditto for dead, but he managed to ring me on his mobile phone. I got there too late to save him but just in time to hear the clue.'

'Why did he keep saying "school dinner"?'

'I haven't the faintest idea. Perhaps you'll find that out.'

It all seems rather unreal: Ditto missing at least, probably dead, the crazy driving, your strange companion so calm and mysterious. Fortunately for you the car screeches to a stop, leaving black tyre marks behind on the road. You're by a phone-box. Ms Noname leans towards you.

'Listen carefully,' she says, perfectly calmly. 'If they can kill him, they can kill me. If that happens only you will be left to prevent the next murder. I'm going to contact our chief and pass on the body. Then I'm going home to change. You mustn't come any further in case my flat and Ditto's house are being watched by *them*. I'm also going to change my phone as a precaution in case they're tapping the calls. Here's a new number for you to ring if you need me in a hurry.' She gives you a card with a new mobile-phone number on it. 'Then,' she continues, 'I'll put the heavy brigade on red alert in case the going gets really tough.'

'Who are the heavy brigade?'

'They've got shooters.'

'Shooters?'

'Yep. Heavy metal. The gun team.' You gulp. You feel as if you're getting right out of your depth in this case.

'What should I do next?'

'That's up to you. As a matter of fact,' she says to your amazement, 'I'm working on two other cases at

30

the moment and one of them is just hotting up. That's why we want you to get on with this. The phone-box might come in useful.'

She smiles, and you realize that she's indicating that your ride's over. You get out, slightly unsteady on your feet but relieved to be on firm ground again. Ms Noname waves and in a second or two is gone. The car is already just a distant sight. You think about her words, 'If they can kill him, they can kill me.' If they can kill her, can they also kill you?

You look around to see whether the phone-box is being watched, but there's no-one in sight except the driver of a bus parked nearby. All its indicators are flashing and 'SORRY I'M NOT IN SERVICE' is showing on the destination board. The driver's sitting inside reading a newspaper, presumably waiting for a breakdown van to arrive.

You go into the phone-box and ring Quicksolve. Your assistant has already arrived back in your car and sets off to pick you up. While you're waiting you must decide where to go next. It looks as if you're on your own on this case now. You reckon you know enough about school dinner already so you don't need to investigate that any further. But you must remember that strange clue in case it makes sense later.

Your choices are:

• To visit a friend of yours who's a police constable and talk to him about Noname and Ditto, by going to page 32.

• To spend an hour with Lizzie Jones, if you have not already done so, to find out more about the Salvation Army, by going to page 17. Without basic information you might not spot a clue if it hit you.

• To find out more about how the Salvation Army helps people in trouble, by going to page 41.

• To look up Lord Carntsey in *Who's Who*, by going to page 22.

You visit a friend who's a police constable

Your friend lives in a police house in a nearby village. After ringing to check that he's at home, you drive down for a chat about Noname and Ditto.

'Ah well,' your friend announces when you've told him about your mysterious visitors, 'there *are* people doing work that's very hush-hush.' He looks around and lowers his voice. 'You see, there's the Security Service, better known as MI5, although it's not part of Military Intelligence at all. It's concerned with counter-espionage.

'Special Branch is part of us,' he adds proudly, 'part of the police force, based at Scotland Yard. Its officers carry out the arrests and do some of the work for MI5. Then there's Interpol, that's an international police link across about a hundred and fifty countries, based at Lyon in France. We also have MI6, the Secret Intelligence Service, but I'm not sure what it does, exactly. It's all top secret, national security, that sort of thing.'

'So Special Branch wouldn't deal with an ordinary murder attempt, if there is such a thing as an ordinary murder?'

'Not unless there was something bigger behind it, like spying. Otherwise, if they came across information about a murder plot, they'd pass it on.'

They'd pass it on. This seems to be exactly what Ms Noname has done. Maybe she, or Ditto, stumbled across this plot in their other work and she's pushed it out to Quicksolve because it isn't really a national or international security matter at all. This thought makes you feel better about the case.

You realize that your friend can't give you any further help. You say goodbye and leave.

Add 1 hour to your time score.

- If you know nothing about Lord Carntsey, you must look him up in *Who's Who* now, by going to page 22.

If you have already done this, you have two choices:

- You could try to meet Lord Carntsey and find out more about him, by going to page 34. If you decide to do this, you will have to **add 2 hours to your time score.**

- You could find out more about how the Salvation Army helps people in trouble. This might provide you with vital background information on the case. To explore this, telephone your Salvationist friend Lizzie, by going to page 41.

Who's Who lists Lord Carntsey's address and phone number. His house isn't far away. You ring him to check that he's at home, then set off.

You arrive at Lord Carntsey's house and ring the bell. To your surprise, he answers it himself. There's no butler, so at least this won't be a murder mystery where the butler does it! You're still hoping that with your help it will turn out to be a murder mystery without a murder as well. Lord Carntsey is smartly dressed and rather solemn, except that he's wearing bright-red carpet-slippers. He takes you into the lounge and sits you by a huge pot plant which looks rather poorly.

'I've been expecting you,' he begins, 'ever since I met that young woman. Never did catch her name. Dressed all in black she was. Anyway she called and warned me you might be coming and that there was some plot or other. How can I help you?'

'Tell me about your work for the Salvation Army,'
you ask.

'Well,' he begins, 'I'm not a member, but I go on
their soup runs. I go down to one of their centres for
the homeless every Christmas and try to give the
people there a good time. I also give talks to some of
my colleagues in industry about the Salvation Army's
work.'

'What for?'

'Money. Fund-raising. Some of my colleagues and
their companies are pretty wealthy but even they
forget that providing 22 400 beds for homeless people
and doing meals for the elderly and trying to re-unite
families and visiting hospitals and prisons costs
money. It's big money, when you add it all up, so I try
to help to raise some of it.'

'You've given the Salvation Army a lot of money
yourself?'

'Ah,' he says modestly, looking around the small
lounge, 'what's money for except to give away? I don't
need that much. Why hang on to it?' You stare at him
open mouthed.

'You see,' he continues, smiling at your amazement,
'to me Christianity's a very simple matter. Jesus said
there were only two essential things you had to do.
The first was to love God with all your heart and all
your soul and all your mind and all your strength.
That's the easy bit – no-one can check on that except
God! The other thing Jesus said we should do was to
love our neighbour as ourselves. He told the parable of
the Good Samaritan to explain what he meant.'

'The Samaritan was good because he helped a man
who'd been beaten up by robbers, didn't he?'

'That's right, but there's a bit more to the story than
that. You see, to lots of Jews of Jesus' day the only
good Samaritan was a dead one, and the feeling was
mutual! Jesus was telling this story to a Jewish

audience. He made the hero a Samaritan to show that people we don't think about or even dislike are our neighbours.'

'Sounds like you're a bit of a good Samaritan yourself with the charity work you do.'

'I try. The Samaritans today take their name from Jesus' story. They run a crisis telephone help line .'

'What other charity things are you involved in?'

'I go into pubs to sell *The War Cry* – the Salvation Army newspaper. That raises a bit of money, but more important, it means we meet people and get chatting.'

'And you can enjoy a few drinks as you go?'

'Not at all! Members of the Army promise never to drink alcohol or smoke. Although I'm not a full member I don't mind keeping those rules.'

'Why do they take that line on drink?'

'Well, in Victorian England when the Army started, alcohol was a major social problem – much like it is today. Booth and the founders of the Army thought that by keeping off it they'd provide a witness. They'd be living evidence of the fact that you don't need booze to make you happy, whether you're at a party or a club or out with your friends. That made it easier for ex-alcoholics to join the Army because they knew they wouldn't be tempted again. After all, alcohol is a drug.'

'No smoking as well?'

'Well, the nicotine in tobacco is a drug too, and nowadays we know all about the harm smoking can do. One of the first Christians, Paul, says in one of his letters that our body is a temple for the Holy Spirit. Poisoning your body by smoking's a fine way to look after a temple!'

'You're not a member of the Salvation Army, so you could smoke?'

'I could, in the sense that I haven't promised not to, but I don't anyway. Funny how many young smokers there are, though, isn't it? They know more than anyone about the health risks.'

'So what can you do? National Lottery?'

He laughs. 'Another no! Remember that all gambling's based on greed – getting something for nothing. For one person to win a fortune, just think how many people have to lose. Some of the people buying Lottery tickets every week are poor people who can't afford to gamble at all. Also, gambling's like smoking and alcohol. It can become addictive and then it destroys people and families.'

'You're not left with much to enjoy!'

'That's where you're wrong! We're left with lots of things to enjoy – friendship, marriage, family, outings, parties ...'

'With no alcohol?'

'No alcohol but lots of friends and people to meet. Then we get pleasure out of helping people. After all, what are we doing with our lives? Just behaving selfishly, or doing something for others?' You'd like to discuss this further with him, but you're aware that it's taking you off the subject you've come about.

'We know that smoking or alcohol or any addiction can kill, but why would anyone want to kill you?'

'I've been thinking about that. In my will, the Salvation Army receives a large donation. What's left of my personal fortune will go to my family, including the businesses – they keep adding money faster than I can give it away! That just leaves the Carntsey Patent.'

'The Carntsey Patent?'

'Yes. It's the formula for a new industrial process – I've worked on it myself.'

'What sort of formula?'

'Chemical. Printed out, there are about fifty pages of notes.'

'What does it do?'

'It's a replacement fuel to power cars. It's based on detoxification and recycling of a chemical mix of domestic waste products.'

'Is it in commercial production?'

'No. But it could be in five or six years.'

'What's it worth?'

'Millions, I suppose, but I've never thought about it like that. To me it's a way of helping the planet.'

'If you die, who gets it?'

'My factory operations general manager, Tom Davies, gets the formula. It's actually on a computer disk and not in a notebook. Tom's been instructed in the event of my death to develop it for the good of the firm and the people who work there. I want them to get the benefits, but it's much simpler legally to leave it all to him.'

'Mmm. Now, I understand you're attending a Salvation Army concert tomorrow?'

'Yes, it's going to be held in the evening at the central hall.'

'What sort of concert?'

'A mixture. Classical brass music, some jazz and pop, some sacred songs.'

'Who's playing?'

'An American Salvation Army band over here on tour. I've heard them play before, when I've been in the States on business. They're quite something.'

'Where is the hall?'

'Not far – a short walk.'

'What's it like for security?'

'Do you want to go and see for yourself? I'll come too and show you the way, if you like.'

This has been a long interview and a very well-spent two hours.

Add 2 hours to your time score.

You now have three choices:

- You could go with Lord Carntsey to the hall where the concert will be held. To do this, go to page 40.

- You could find out more about how the Salvation Army helps people in trouble. This might provide you with vital background information on the case. To explore this, telephone your Salvationist friend Lizzie, by going to page 41.

- If you think it might not be safe for Lord Carntsey to go out to the hall, you could pretend that you've another call to make first and visit the hall on your own. To do this, go to page 47.

You decide to go with Lord Carntsey to the hall

As you get up to go with Lord Carntsey, his telephone rings. He picks up the receiver:

'Hello.' There's a pause then he hands it over. 'It's for you.'

'Don't be such a fool,' says a muffled female voice you seem to vaguely recognize. 'It's too risky. Leave him in the house. Make an excuse to leave by yourself straight away.' You replace the phone and think about this anonymous advice.

'Er, I can't go to the hall for a bit. Look, er, would you mind staying here for now? I've got another call to make first.' You shake hands with Lord Carntsey and leave.

Who made the phone call and how did she know what was about to happen? Was it Ms Noname again? How could she have known what was happening? Is the room bugged? Or are you?

Choose again:

- You could visit the hall on your own, by going to page 47.

- You could find out more about how the Salvation Army helps people in trouble. This might provide you with vital background information on the case. To explore this, telephone your Salvationist friend Lizzie, by going to page 41.

You find out more about how the Salvation Army helps people in trouble

A phone call to Lizzie Jones gives you some instant answers. She reads out from a booklet a surprising range of work done by the Army in about ninety countries:

In the UK:
- among alcoholics and drug abusers, 71 homes and 38 day centres;
- among the homeless, in food distribution centres and overnight hostels;
- in visiting those in prison (375 000 visits in one year!);
- helping those released from prison who have nowhere to live and no job to go to and are therefore at high risk of re-offending to get money;
- in providing a listening ear, either in person or in the Listening Ear column of *The War Cry*, or via counselling services for those with personal problems;
- helping youngsters who've run away from home, often to London, and find themselves in danger on the streets;
- in tracing separated members of a family;
- in night patrol, rescue and anti-suicide work;
- running eventide homes (homes for the elderly);
- running children's homes and holiday homes, also day nurseries and crèches;
- running mobile canteens for servicemen and women, e.g. at the site of disasters where the regular army is called in to provide help;
- providing family welfare services and advice.

In other countries:
- running 50 hospitals, 130 clinics, 22 specialist maternity hospitals or clinics, 1100 schools, 8 teacher-training schools ...

The list goes on, but you're only half listening. You're thinking about all the work that goes into the activities you've already heard about. Why do they do it? Lizzie finishes reading so you ask her this question.

'It's to do with what we call "compassion in action",' she replies. 'There's a bit about that in another booklet. Hang on a second ... here's what it says.' She reads you two more paragraphs.

Compassion in action

In the name of Christ and in the spirit of its founder, William Booth, the Salvation Army offers practical help, spiritually motivated. Young, old, rich, poor, black, white ... None of the distinctions count with the Salvation Army. Salvationists see only a child of God in need of help.

To do all this the Salvation Army counts on the active support of its officers and members, then the support of the others who attend it as their 'church', even if they aren't members, then the wider group still of people who support it by making financial donations at street collections or in pubs or in responding to magazine or newspaper appeals.

This glimpse of the range of the Army's work and their reasons for doing it reminds you that no religion is just about beliefs. Religions are about beliefs being translated into daily action.

'Why don't you come and see us in action for yourself?' suggests Lizzie. 'There's a meeting on now, but when it finishes we'll be setting off on some of the visits I've been reading about.'

Choose:

- You could go with Lizzie to see the Army in action, by turning to page 44.

- If you have not already looked up Lord Carntsey in *Who's Who*, you could do so now, by turning to page 22.

- If you have looked up Lord Carntsey in *Who's Who*, you could try to meet him, if you have not already done so, by turning to page 34.

- If you have been to Lord Carntsey's house, you could visit the hall where the concert will be held by turning to page 47.

You go with Lizzie to see the Army in action

You arrive back at Ecclesfield citadel to find a meeting (or service) just finishing. There are about twenty people, not all in uniform. Lizzie tells you that more people attend on Sundays, but this is mid-week so this group is mainly retired or unwaged people. They're just finishing enthusiastic singing of a chorus hymn, accompanied by one uniformed member playing a keyboard and another beating the rhythm with a tambourine. Lizzie's mum is at the front as the leader or speaker. As the people sit down she asks them informally:

'Now does anyone want to give us a word of praise for what's happened to them since the last meeting? Something you want to thank the Lord for, some blessing?' An elderly woman calls out something you don't quite hear, but Mrs Captain Jones does.

'Yes, thank you, Mabel,' she replies. 'Mabel wants to say a word of praise for her grandson's recovery after his operation. Anyone else? Don't be shy!'

A man calls out, 'Thanks for life and food.'

'Yes, praise the Lord for life and food. Let's thank him now,' says Mrs Captain Jones. The people in the meeting close their eyes and so does she.

'Dear Loving God, thank you for calling us and thank you for finding us when we were lost and for speaking to us in Jesus,' she begins. You hear a few people murmuring 'Mmmm' or 'Amen' or 'Yes, yes.' 'And especially today, dear Lord, we give you thanks for Mabel's grandson's recovery and, as Fred reminded us, for life and food ...'

As she continues to lead the prayer, you feel that it's very informal and very sincere. Before you've properly

switched back into it again, the meeting has ended
and people are chatting in groups or leaving. A
number seem to be heading for their cars. Lizzie
travels with you and directs you into the run-down
part of the city.

'There's no soup,' you say, surprised.

'We don't do the soup run till evening,' she
explains, 'we're on vouchers now.'

'Vouchers?'

As you talk she shows you where to park and you

regroup with about a dozen of the Army ready to walk the streets. It's a tour of doorways and subways and back alleys. The group know their route well. You soon find people sitting or lying on the ground. Some have cans of alcohol, usually empty, around them. Most are, not surprisingly, dirty. Some have ragged bundles of possessions or caps for money set out on the pavement. You stick with Lizzie. She greets all the people with a smile and hello, and knows some by name. She gives each person a sheet of printed paper and wishes them 'God bless' as she moves on.

'We don't give money,' she explains, 'because some of them would spend it on alcohol. Instead, we have an arrangement with several local fish and chip shops and take-away burger places. They can hand in the voucher there and get a hot meal to the value printed on it. The owners send the vouchers back to us and we pay the bill. So the homeless people get at least a hot meal.'

Some of the people you meet have dogs. Lizzie has a packet of biscuits and gives them a few for the dog. She tells one or two that the Salvation Army clothing store can provide something warm for them to wear and when it will be open. You don't remember all the people, but you do remember what one old woman calls out, after a fit of coughing, as Lizzie is walking away.

'Angels. That's what you lot are. B***** angels.'

Return to the page you came from and make another choice:

- If you came here after talking to Lizzie on the phone, return to page 43.
- If you came here after interviewing the four suspects, return to page 63.
- If you came here after analysing those interviews, return to page 65.

You visit the hall where the concert will be held

The hall isn't far from Lord Carntsey's house. You go in through an entrance area with a staircase off it at each side. Ahead of you are double swing-doors which lead into the main body of the hall at ground-floor level. Ignoring the notices and the list of times of meetings (services) in the entrance area, you go straight through the swing-doors.

The main hall is much bigger than you expected. On three sides there is a gallery at first-floor level, with rows of bench seats for perhaps two hundred people. On the ground floor there are enough chairs to seat another three hundred – plenty of room here for the concert.

At the front there's a raised platform with a railing. You spot a bench below it with the words GOD IS

LOVE painted on in capital letters. Above the platform are seats rising up in rows. Those on your left have music stands in front of them and those on the right don't. You guess that the band will sit on the left with perhaps a choir on the right. To your surprise, there's no organ as you would expect in most churches. Then you remember Lizzie telling you that the band plays at Sunday services and that organs aren't used.

'Hello. I'm Fred Schudanner – I'm the bandmaster.' You turn round to see a red-faced, plump man in his

mid-forties, in Salvation Army uniform. He's holding his hand out for you to shake and as you do so he gives your hand a hearty squeeze. You gasp slightly, wondering how many bones he's broken and whether he was ever a professional wrestler. You can tell from his accent that he's American or Canadian.

'You must be the janitor,' he says. You gulp, but as you're about to correct him, he continues, 'Well, the band will sit on your left, of course,' so you were right, 'and the songsters will be left with the seats on the right.' You try to work this out.

'Er, how many?' you ask.

'Twenty in the band and forty-three in the songsters,' Fred beams.

'And they're all your regular people?'

'That's not what janitors usually ask me when we're on tour,' he replies. 'Actually they are regulars, except with this flu bug going round we've had to get a few extras to replace sick folk.'

'A few? How many?'

'You do ask some funny questions. Four actually. Three to cover flu and one to cover a long-term absence, all in the band as it happens.'

'But you know them all personally?'

'No, I haven't met any of them before. They're coming from different bands in other parts of the UK. I've flown in from the States to conduct the concert.'

'Would you mind telling me who the replacements are?'

'Would you mind telling me who *you* are? You're a very weird janitor.' You show him your Quicksolve identity card. Briefly you explain that you've been asked to check security for Lord Carntsey's visit. That's why you want to know about the four replacement players. Fred appears delighted to be able to help you and gets out a piece of paper from his pocket.

'I wrote their names down,' he says proudly,

49

Joyce Crabtree, trumpet, from Belfast

Janet Fielding, tuba, from Bradford

John Matthews, trombone, from Dundee

Eric Webster, timpani, from Swansea

'because I knew I might not remember them. We've brought in the best from bands all over the UK. They're coming early to meet me here.'

You jot down this list in your notebook. Thanking Fred, you go and sit on one of the seats as the real caretaker comes in. He starts to make detailed arrangements with Fred about who will sit where and what will happen when at the concert.

You think over what you know. There's likely to be an attack on Lord Carntsey at the performance tomorrow. He'll be in the front row of the audience with his friends. There will be sixty-three performers on the platform, plus Fred conducting. All but four of the performers are regulars and know each other, so anyone new would be noticed by the other members of the band or the songsters. Fred doesn't know any of the four newcomers brought in for the occasion. They may not know each other. The other members of the group may not have met them before. There's got to be a good chance that a professional killer might kidnap one of the substitute players and send in their own man – or woman – instead.

You think further about the replacement players and their instruments. The killer could smuggle in a weapon using a tuba case or a trombone case ... or hide it inside a drum. A trumpet case would be smaller ... but still possible.

Choose:

- Whether to spend an hour back at the Quicksolve office checking what weapons could be hidden in instrument cases of this sort. If you decide to do this, you will have to **add 1 hour to your time score**, but it might help you to work out what type of weapon you might be looking for. To check up on possible weapons, go to page 53.

- Whether to ring Ms Noname at the last number she gave you and try to arrange a meeting to discuss where you go from here. To do this, turn to page 52.

You ring Ms Noname

To your delight, she answers the call on her mobile phone straight away.

'I was wondering if we could meet?' you ask.

'No problem,' she replies, 'I'm sitting right outside in the car.' You're very surprised to find she's so near and you waste no time in joining her. Briefly you update her on what you've found out, especially about the four replacement members of the band.

'What do you advise?' you ask. She thinks for a moment or two, then her face lights up.

'Got it!' she says. 'Why don't you interview all four replacement players one at a time? Ask them questions about Christianity and the Salvation Army. Whoever's been put in to kill Lord Carntsey is bound to fail the test. They'll give some answer that doesn't make sense or they'll keep avoiding the questions. That way you'll know they're an imposter.'

You get out of the car and think about Ms Noname. Can you trust her?

Choose now:

- Whether to check what weapons could be hidden in the replacement players' instrument cases. If you decide to do this, you will have to **add 1 hour to your time score**, but it might help you to work out what weapon you might be looking for. To check up on possible weapons, go to page 53.

- Whether to start to interview the four replacement players. To do this, go to page 58.

- Whether to use some books your assistant has collected to add to your knowledge of what the Salvation Army does, if you haven't already done so. If you choose this option, you will have to **add 1 hour to your time score**, but it might be time very well spent if you want to catch out a guilty person in an interview. To do this extra research turn to page 56, but first **bookmark this page** so that you can return to it afterwards.

You check up on possible weapons

Add 1 hour to your time score.

You consult Nigel, one of your Quicksolve staff who until recently served as a gunner in the army (the military army, not the Salvation Army!). He has a good knowledge of weapons.

'Well,' he begins, 'forget the comics and the novels. I'll tell you the real-life possibilities. Your killer isn't likely to bring a shotgun – too heavy and too unreliable if it's a serious assassination attempt.' You start wondering what the opposite of a serious assassination attempt might be, but quickly stop this and listen to Nigel again.

'With a shotgun you'd get only one shot before reloading so you'd probably have to try to escape fast. To be accurate a shotgun would need a barrel at least 60 cm long – not easy to hide. Terrorists often use automatic weapons. These can fire up to 1200 rounds of ammunition per minute, but they can and do jam, fortunately for the people who're being shot at! Rifles are more accurate, but like shotguns, the longer the barrel, the better the accuracy. They're equally hard to hide.

'Handguns are much easier to conceal, but much less accurate, despite the cowboy films where they shoot from the waist with one hand without aiming and still hit the bad guy! The smallest weapon of all to conceal would be some sort of explosive device. KGB Department 14 used to specialize in small assassination devices. I don't know what they're up to now – perhaps some have been sold off in the West.'

'I'm picturing a situation with a potential killer

sitting on a platform in full public view,' you explain. 'The target will be sitting in the front row of the audience.'

'So if your killer uses a gun he or she will have to stand up, use two hands and take aim?' You nod.

'If she – or he – is on the platform,' Nigel continues, 'they'll probably be stopped before they can fire, or the target will have a chance to run or duck or avoid the shot.'

'Mmm.'

'On the other hand an explosive device could blow up the killer and leave the target unharmed.'

'Mmm.'

'Unless the killer threw it.'

'It would still need aiming?'

'Of course.'

'What about "way out" methods? Poisoned darts, that sort of thing?' you ask.

'Crazy!' Nigel laughs. 'Your killer isn't going to stand up and take aim with a blow-pipe or something similar while the target sits quietly waiting to see if the dart hits him!'

'Could one be blown from a musical instrument?'

'That's a new one on me. In theory it could be, if the instrument was carefully adapted, but it would still need aiming. There'd have to be a "sight" on the top of the instrument to aim with, like you have on top of a gun. But I've never heard of anything like that being used. It sounds more like fiction.'

'How about a poisoned hypodermic needle? That's been used in real life.'

'Yes, but how's your killer going to get near enough?'

'Mmm. I'll have to think all this over. Thanks for your help.' As you turn to go, Nigel calls after you, 'Are you sure your killer's going to be on the platform?'

You think about what Nigel has said. *Are* you sure? Which of these is the most likely method of attack? Can you think of others?

Choose now:

- Whether to ring Ms Noname, if you haven't just done so, and try to arrange a meeting to discuss where you go from here. To do this, turn to page 52.

- Whether to use some books your assistant has collected to brief yourself on the Salvation Army in more detail. If you choose this option, you will have to **add 1 hour to your time score**. To add to your knowledge of what the Salvation Army does, turn to page 56, but first **bookmark this page** so that you can return to it afterwards.

- Whether to interview the four replacement players. To do this, turn to page 58.

You add to your knowledge of what the Salvation Army does

Add 1 hour to your time score.

This is what you discover. William Booth, the founder of the Salvation Army, wrote a book in 1890 called *In Darkest England and the Way Out*. In it he attacked the social conditions that helped crime to thrive and that made people desperately poor. In one passage Booth wrote:

> As in Africa streams intersect the forest in every direction, so the gin shop stands at every corner [of UK cities] with its River of the water of Death flowing seventeen hours out of the twenty-four for the destruction of the people ...

He then proposed city colonies, farm colonies and overseas colonies to provide accommodation and jobs and to give human dignity back to people who had lost it. He went on:

> Is it too much to hope that in God's world God's children may be able to do something, if they set to work with a will, to carry out a plan of campaign [you notice the army language again] against these great evils which are the nightmare of our existence?

You discover that one of the 'nightmares' Booth targeted was match manufacture. In his day matches were made using phosphorus, but the price paid was the health and lives of the women working in the

56

match factories. White phosphorus is luminous and highly inflammable – good for matches – but also highly poisonous – bad for people! It gave the workers 'phossy jaw'. Owing to the publicity and pressure from Booth and the Salvationists, the match industry changed to safer chemicals. You wonder what Booth would target in the world now as a nightmare.

All this increases your understanding of the Salvation Army as an organization that tries to put its Christian beliefs into practical action.

Return to the page you came from and make another choice:

- If you had just been checking on weapons, return to page 55.

- If you had just phoned Ms Noname, return to page 52.

You interview the four players

You look for Fred Schudanner and find him talking to two men and two women in Salvation Army uniform.

'Oh, there you are,' he calls to you, 'come and meet the new players.'

'I'd like to talk to you separately,' you explain to them, 'just a matter of a security check, a few questions.' You look keenly at all four suspects, but nobody gives away any worry or concern because you're going to question them. You realize that the criminal must be a pretty cool customer. It's not going to be easy to spot him or her.

'I wonder if we could start alphabetically,' you ask, 'with Joyce Crabtree?' One of the women steps forward and you show her into the caretaker's office, which is empty. He is now busy dusting the bench seats in the gallery. He watches you go into his office, staring rather rudely at you. Perhaps he resents you using it.

There are a couple of chairs and a dust-covered table. Joyce sits facing you. She is in her late twenties, with brown eyes and hair. She looks as if she's blushing. Does that mean she's guilty? But lots of people blush easily. Perhaps it doesn't mean anything at all. You're going to have to watch and listen extremely carefully to all the interviews.

'Could you tell me a bit about how you came to be in the Army?' you ask.

'Well,' she begins, relaxing as she talks, 'my mum and dad took me every week for as far back as I can remember. I've even seen a photo of me as a baby in arms outside the citadel. But when I was a young teenager – thirteen – I went one evening on my own to a rally. The colour-sergeant carried the flag down the hall at the start, then there was an opening song and

58

after that a testimony.' She stops and looks at you, then continues.

'You might not know that a testimony is a sort of witness, evidence, by someone who's become a Christian. It's about some action of the Lord in their life. Well, this testimony was by someone who was a corps assistant. She said that being a follower of Jesus was like being on the fastest, most exciting ride you can go on at a theme park. You never knew what was going to happen next, you had to grab hold, trust the ride and hang on. It was thrills and sometimes spills.

'She said a lot more as well, then there was another song, but her words stuck in my mind. When the time came for prayer, I felt I had to go and kneel at the mercy seat – that's the bench at the front that you can go and kneel in front of during the service. What I was feeling inside was that Jesus was calling me to be a follower of him – really me, not because my parents had decided to take me there every week through my childhood. This was now my own personal decision. I would become a senior soldier as soon as I could.' She grins. 'So I did! I didn't choose Jesus, so much as he chose me.'

You thank Joyce Crabtree for talking to you and show her to the door. Next you invite Janet Fielding, the tuba player, into the little room to talk to you. As you fetch her in you find the caretaker hanging around outside the door, duster in hand, gazing at you. This time you stare at him as rudely as you can and shut the door with a slam to try to encourage him to go away.

Janet Fielding is quite a plump woman, in her fifties, with untidy blonde hair straggling out from under her Army hat. You ask her the same question as you asked Joyce:

'Could you tell me a bit about how you came to be in the Army?'

'I was never enrolled as a junior soldier,' she begins, 'because my parents weren't church-goers. In my childhood I never went to church anywhere at all. I just assumed religion didn't matter because Mum and Dad never talked about it. But when I was about fourteen my gran – she was a Salvationist – was promoted to glory. Oh, sorry,' she grins, 'I should explain that's how we describe death for a Salvationist. It means going to be with the Lord. That's why it's promotion and glory, rather than disaster and the end.

'Anyway, I went to the funeral and that was the first real contact I had with Salvationists. Until then I just thought of them as, well, sort of odd people with collecting-boxes who held services in the open air with their bands. I used to see them at the seaside when we went on holiday. What I found when I met them for real was that they were warm and friendly and human and ...' she giggles.

'Well, one of the boys in the band at the funeral was at the same school as me and he asked me out afterwards. I went to a funeral and got a date! I really fancied him! So we started going out together and I started going with him every week to the Army. He went to three services every Sunday, so it was the only way I could see him then! He was in the band, so I took up playing the tuba and that's how I got involved. Gran would have been pleased if she'd known she'd brought us together!'

'And you eventually married him?' you ask, noticing her wedding ring. She laughs.

'Good gracious, no! I must have gone out with every lad in the corps before I married anyone and then it wasn't him!'

You can't help smiling as you thank her and show her out, but your smile vanishes as you almost fall over the caretaker. He's on his hands and knees on the floor by the door, apparently dusting round the frame.

'*Please* go away. These are private interviews,' you tell him, with a threatening politeness. Maybe you ought to check on him later. He looks very angry and walks away as slowly as he can, to make a point. In comes John Matthews for the next interview. He's a tough-looking man, with close-cropped hair, perhaps about thirty-five. Your notes remind you that he's the trombone player from Dundee.

'Could you tell me how you came to be in the Army?'

'Sure. I was brought up in the Army from a boy, but like a lot of kids I kicked against it as a teenager. I was quite a rebel. I drank heavily and often – cider at first. I smoked like a chimney, bunked off school, got involved in fights in the local gangs, did a bit of joy-riding, a bit of drug taking. The police knew me. I got convictions for petty offences. I was going right off the rails. I was running away – not physically, because I still lived at home – but running away inside. God only knows, and he does, where it might have ended.

'Well, one Sunday night when I was twenty-three I'd already had a good few drinks and I was wandering past a Salvation meeting-hall. It was miles from the one I'd grown up in but hadn't been to for more than ten years. When I heard the noise of the singing drifting out onto the street, I felt it sort of calling me in. It was as if it was saying "Come home". It was raining. I was wet and cold. So I went in and sat on a seat very near the door, so I could leave as quickly as I wanted. But I didn't leave.

'Going to a different meeting was like seeing it all for the first time. I was given a very warm welcome by the people there. They must have smelt the whisky on my breath but took no notice all the same. They helped me to start to see that Jesus isn't some far-away figure of two thousand years ago. I realized that he's here now and was concerned about me and how I was letting myself fall apart.

'After that I couldn't wait for the next Sunday meeting, and the next. The drinking, fighting and all the rest just died away. Who needs to do that if they're happy? What did I need to prove any more? So here I am today,' he smiles, 'and the most violent thing I do now is to blow my trombone.' But he rivals this by blowing his nose with a good honk into his handkerchief.

You thank John Matthews for telling you his story and show him out. This time the caretaker is nowhere in sight. Eric Webster, a pale, rather nervous looking young man, comes into the room as the last of your four suspects.

'Tell me how you came to be in the Army.'

'There's not much to tell. I grew up in it, and I'm in it now.' You're rather surprised. After the stories of the other three, this seems rather flat.

'Did you have any special experience? Any special "leading", do you call it?'

'Not really. I was just content in it, I suppose, so I stayed.' This seems unhelpful.

'What about the music, er, didn't you enjoy that?'

'Yes. That's why I'm in the band.'

'Special religious experiences?'

'Not everyone sees visions,' he says quietly. You give up, thank him and let him leave. He looks relieved.

You now have these choices:

- You could stay in the caretaker's office and try to analyse your four interviews and make some deductions from them, by going to page 64.

- You could check the arrangements for the concert by talking to Fred, the conductor, by going to page 66.

- You could go with Lizzie to see the Army in action, if you have not already done so, by going to page 44. Can you really understand any religion without seeing it at worship and work? Seeing it in action might provide the vital clue. If you decide to do this, **bookmark this page** so that you can return to it afterwards.

You analyse your four interviews

You think first about the blushing Joyce. Did she blush through guilt? Did she use Salvation Army words? Was there an obvious mistake in her story?

Glance back at page 58 if you can't remember her interview, then return to this page.

Next you think about Janet and the story of all her boyfriends. Did she use Salvation Army words? Was there an obvious mistake in her story? Can people 'catch' religion through their boyfriends or girlfriends?

Glance back at page 59 if you can't remember her interview, then return to this page.

Then there was John, the ex-tough guy. Did he use Salvation Army words? Was there an obvious mistake in his story? He's certainly tough enough to be a violent criminal. He admitted that he'd had a violent past, but what does that prove?

Glance back at page 61 if you can't remember his interview, then return to this page.

Finally there was unhelpful Eric, with his short answers. Did he use Salvation Army words? Was there an obvious mistake in what he said? The real problem is that he didn't tell a story at all. What does that mean? It could mean he has something to hide. On the other hand it could just mean he's shy, or that he hasn't a story to tell like the others. He might simply be more ordinary, or he could be the killer ...

Glance back at page 63 if you can't remember his interview, then return to this page.

There are three possible ways to push your detection forward:

- You could interview all four suspects again and ask them more questions to see if you can catch one of them out. To do this, go to page 70.

- You could check the arrangements for the concert in case they provide a clue to how the attack is going to happen. You might get the solution more quickly by chasing the 'how' rather than the 'who'. To do this, talk to the conductor, Fred, by going to page 66.

- Time is running short. This is your last chance to go with Lizzie to see the Army in action, if you have not already done so. It may give you the vital clue. To do this, go to page 44. Before you turn to page 44, **bookmark this page** so that you can return to it afterwards.

You check the arrangements for the concert

Friendly, helpful Fred comes across when he sees you looking in his direction. You take him into the caretaker's office so that the others can't hear you.

'What exactly are the arrangements for the concert?' you ask.

'Well,' he begins, 'the rest of the performers are due to arrive tomorrow. We've never played in this particular hall so we'll need a good rehearsal. Tom, the janitor, who's new himself, has made the arrangements for dressing-rooms and so on. We brought in the four new players earlier so they could get used to the hall and do some separate practising in what's left of today. Lord Carntsey is the sponsor of the show. He wants to meet all the players in the band, so we thought it would be a nice idea if he could come to meet these four today.' You weren't expecting that.

'And can he?'

'Sure! I'm delighted to say he can come and he'll be here very shortly. They're each going to play a short solo for him – except the timpani, of course! Then we'll all have a cuppa together.'

You need to think fast. Ms Noname could be wrong in thinking that an assassination attempt will occur at the concert. It could be easier to strike in the nearly empty hall when Lord Carntsey comes to meet the four replacement players.

What about the caretaker, Tom? You've heard that name somewhere before, but is that just coincidence? He's certainly been all ears for what you've been up to.

Choose:

- Whether to try to analyse your four interviews with the replacement players and make some deductions from them, if you haven't already done so, by going to page 64.

- Whether to interview all four suspects again and ask them more questions, by going to page 70.

- Whether to spend an hour trying to work out where you've heard the name Tom, by going to page 68. If you decide to do this, **bookmark this page** so that you can return to it afterwards.

You think about where you've heard the name Tom

Add 1 hour to your time score.

Why does that name ring a bell? As you puzzle about this your thoughts return to Tom the caretaker. He's behaving suspiciously, trying to listen in to what's going on, including your interviews. What does that prove? That he's the killer? Or that he's very nosey? Or bored?

Perhaps you've concentrated too much on the killer, instead of the motive. Could the motive lead you to the killer? Have you started at the wrong end in this case?

Why would anyone want to kill Lord Carntsey? He seems such a kind and good man. Who would benefit from his death? Would he, or she, or they, benefit enough to make it worth killing him?

Suppose someone wanted to kill Lord Carntsey for big money, would they kill him in person? Or would they hire someone to do it for them? Ms Noname seems to think the killer is a professional hit man – or woman. If that's the case, Lord Carntsey will not recognize the killer when he arrives at the rehearsal, because they will not have met before. But if the killer is a hired person, they'll be less likely to blunder. Also, the real criminal – whoever hired them – could have a cast-iron alibi by being miles away, or even abroad, at the time of the killing.

Perhaps you should try to identify two people, the killer and the mind behind the plot.

Return to page 67 and make another choice.

You ring the Quicksolve office

You go out to your car and dial the number. To your annoyance all you get is the Boss, speaking in a posh voice:

'This is the Quicksolve Detective Agency. I'm sorry there's no-one to take your call, as the office is empty, but if you'd like to leave a message after the tone, we'll ring you as soon as we can ...' You put the phone down on this recorded message.

Down the road you notice a parked bus. It looks vaguely familiar. That's not surprising, since different bus companies use buses in the same colours, but parked buses are less usual. This one has 'SORRY I'M NOT IN SERVICE' on the destination indicator. The driver is sitting reading a newspaper. Perhaps he's early for his next run and is taking a break. Have you seen something like that before? What does it mean?

Pondering all this, you return to the hall.

Go to page 76.

You interview the four suspects again

You need much clearer evidence before you can work out which of the players might be the killer. Your first interviews have raised your suspicions, but you need more. Maybe letting the suspects tell you their stories wasn't such a good idea, as it allowed them to choose what to say to you. Any of them could have learnt a story like the one they told, without it being true ... except that one didn't tell a story at all. This time you decide to ask the suspects more detailed questions so that they won't be able to say anything they like. They'll have to give right or wrong answers. It will also be a good idea to get them to write down their answers so that you can compare them afterwards.

You decide to ring Lizzie Jones and ask her the sorts of thing you might ask. That way you'll get the questions right. You pop outside to use your car-phone so that you can't be overheard by that nosey caretaker, who seems to be shadowing various people around the hall. Fortunately you get through to Lizzie immediately. You have to wait a few minutes for her to think up suitable questions and check with her mum, who happens to be at home as well. You soon return to the hall with a list of questions and an outline of the right answers.

'I'm sorry to pester you further,' you explain to the four puzzled musicians, 'but as a final security check I must ask you to answer these five short questions in writing now.'

'Well you can ask, but I'm not writing anything! I object to being treated like a criminal.' The speaker is Janet Fielding. She feels so strongly that she's already striding towards the door to leave. What has she to hide?

'I'm sorry,' you call to her, 'but if you walk out on this, you walk out on the chance to play in the concert. We do have very good reasons for these security precautions.'

'Huh!' She stomps back, looking very angry, and sits down again.

'I'm not so happy about it either.' This time the speaker is John Matthews, the ex-tough guy. 'We don't *have* to cooperate with this.'

'It's entirely up to you,' you reply, 'but I've been brought in because it is more than possible that a serious crime might be committed here. We've got to vet everybody.'

'Yes,' adds the beaming Fred to help you out, 'it's in the interests of the innocent to cooperate in this, so as to identify the guilty. It won't take long.'

'Looks like we've got no real choice, having come all this way to perform in the concert,' says Joyce Crabtree. You're irritated to notice the caretaker nodding his agreement in the background. What's it got to do with him? You tear out sheets from your notepad and borrow four ballpoint pens from the office for the musicians to use. Then you read out each question, pausing to give them time to write down their answers.

1. Where are the Salvation Army Territorial Headquarters for the UK?
2. What are the Articles of War?
3. How many Articles of War are there?
4. What does the Army believe about baptism?
5. Complete this part of Article 4: We believe that Jesus Christ is 'truly and properly God and ...'

You watch the players as they jot down their answers. Eric Webster seems to have written least. His eyes dart about suspiciously. Is he trying to read Joyce's answers? Fred is hanging round nervously to see the result of the test you've set. The caretaker is leaning on his sweeping brush, idly watching all of you.

As you collect the answer sheets, you think about the situation up to now. In the interviews, the least convincing person was Eric Webster. But it was Janet Fielding and John Matthews who protested about doing the written test.

You compare the four sets of answers. One person has matched almost word for word the answers Lizzie gave you: Janet Fielding. You check the others carefully for mistakes, using hers as a blueprint answer. Slightly to your annoyance you find Fred trying to read the answers over your shoulder.

'Who's done worst? Have you discovered the villain?' he asks eagerly. The caretaker has walked nearer to listen in.

'I'm still thinking,' you reply.

'Well, come and see what I've found while you've just been thinking,' says Fred, with a note of triumph in his voice.

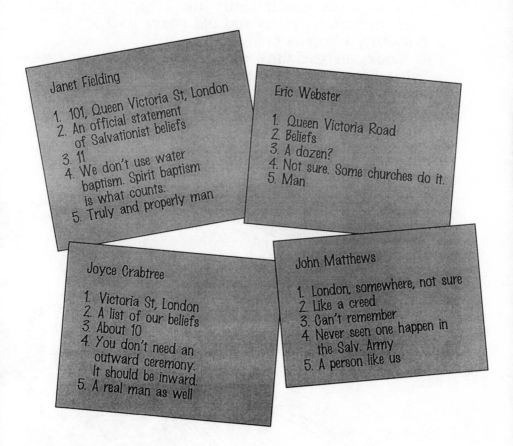

Janet Fielding
1. 101, Queen Victoria St, London
2. An official statement of Salvationist beliefs
3. 11
4. We don't use water baptism. Spirit baptism is what counts.
5. Truly and properly man

Eric Webster
1. Queen Victoria Road
2. Beliefs
3. A dozen?
4. Not sure. Some churches do it.
5. Man

Joyce Crabtree
1. Victoria St, London
2. A list of our beliefs
3. About 10
4. You don't need an outward ceremony. It should be inward.
5. A real man as well

John Matthews
1. London, somewhere, not sure
2. Like a creed
3. Can't remember
4. Never seen one happen in the Salv. Army
5. A person like us

Choose:

- Whether to go with Fred and see what he's discovered, by turning to page 74.

- Whether to ring the Quicksolve office to see if you can find out anything further about the nosey caretaker, by turning to page 69.

You go with Fred

Fred leads you triumphantly into a back room where there are music stands and old boxes stacked up. It's obviously a storeroom.

'Look,' he exclaims, opening an instrument case, 'what do you say to this?' You're looking at a pistol, about 28 cm long, lying inside the case.

'It's an M10!' he tells you excitedly. It's a trumpet case that it's turned up in. The label on the outside of the case reads quite clearly 'Joyce Crabtree.' It's her case, but does that mean she put the gun in there?

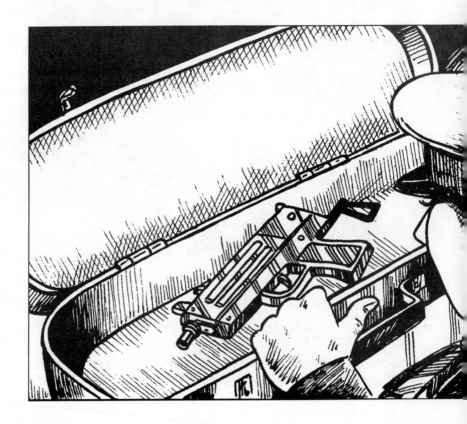

Choose:

- You could arrest Joyce Crabtree straight away. If you do, you must first write down your solution to the case. Remember, you need to get right:

  - the name of the killer,

  - the motive or reason for the assassination attempt,

  - the method the killer is planning to use.

  You will then move directly to the solution page of the book, so if you are wrong you will have lost the case altogether. To arrest Joyce Crabtree, **write down your full solution** then go straight to page 84.

- You could ring the Quicksolve office to see if you can find out anything further about the nosey caretaker. To do this, go to page 69.

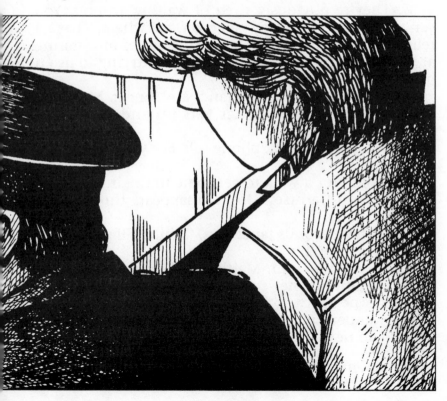

You return to the hall

Fred comes running up to greet you, glad to see you back. 'Just in time! Just in time!' he says. 'Lord Carntsey will be here in a quarter of an hour to meet the new players and watch them rehearse. They're going to play some solos.' He pauses.

'Isn't it about time you arrested someone?' he asks eagerly. You feel rather pressured by this attitude.

'In good time, in good time,' you reply, looking around. The four musicians are sitting chatting together. They look in your direction as if to see whether you've cleared them from a security point of view. They're obviously tired of waiting around. You can't see Tom, the nosey caretaker, anywhere. That's a relief. You were getting rather suspicious of him staring at you all the time and loitering around trying to listen in to the interviews.

'Well, I can't wait for clearance any longer. Must pop to the Gents.' Eric Webster gets up and leaves the room.

'I must make a quick phone call. See you soon.' Fred hurries off.

'I'm going for a walk to get some fresh air before we play for Lord Carntsey.' Joyce disappears through the entrance doors.

After a few seconds Janet says, 'I think I'll go and see if I can catch her up.'

This just leaves John Matthews. He takes out a copy of the Salvationist newspaper. 'I'll just have a read and stay here,' he says.

You wander out into the entrance area and wonder what to do next.

As you re-enter the hall a few minutes later, you meet a white-faced Eric Webster. He looks at you and says only the words: 'The storeroom. The storeroom.' You rush past him into the corridor leading to the Gents. The storeroom door is wide open. Lying on the floor on his back, face up, is the caretaker. He has been shot in the chest. He's clearly dead. On the floor by the door is a handgun. An empty trumpet case has been thrown down beside the body.

As you're staring at the scene, in some shock yourself, you become aware of Joyce Crabtree standing next to you in the doorway. She looks pale but quite calm. Did she hide the gun in that trumpet case?

Before you can decide what to do next you hear Fred calling in the distance:

'Lord Carntsey! His Lordship's arrived! Come and meet Lord Carntsey, everybody.'

Lord Carntsey's life is indeed in danger with a killer in the building. You can't afford to investigate the death of the caretaker for the moment. You leave the storeroom and hurry Joyce into the main hall, where you recognize Lord Carntsey coming through the swing-doors. The living need protection now – before they join the dead!

You have an immediate choice:

- If you want to make an arrest, you must first write down your solution to the case. Remember, you need to get right:

  - the name of the killer,

  - the motive or reason for the assassination attempt,

  - the method the killer is planning to use.

  You will then move directly to the solution page of the book. If you're right about who to arrest, you will have saved Lord Carntsey's life without any further trouble. If you're wrong, you will have lost the case and left Lord Carntsey in the room with the real killer. If you want to make an arrest, **write down your full solution** then go straight to page 84.

- If you're not ready to make an arrest, read on but be prepared to act quickly as events unfold further.

In the hall Lord Carntsey takes off his coat and sits down. His red carpet-slippers have been replaced by well-polished shoes. Fred has gone off to make everyone 'a nerve-calming cup of tea', as he puts it. The players are tuning up, getting their instruments ready to perform their solos, except for Eric the drummer. He's sitting watching you, still white faced and deeply shocked. Joyce is behaving normally. Either the shock hasn't hit her yet, or she's very much in control of events. You daren't leave the room in case

one of them attempts to kill Lord Carntsey.

As you watch the four players like a hawk you find yourself thinking hard. The caretaker is dead in the back room – shot. Why? Did he discover something while he was snooping, something so important that he was killed? Your mind goes back to Ditto. Two people are now dead. With two corpses already, your work on the case is starting to look a bit careless, but you seem to be up against a real professional killer – someone cool and convincing, but who?

While your mind is racing with what to do, you become aware that there's someone in the gallery above you watching. This person is sitting very cleverly with the evening light from the windows shining behind him – or her – so you can't see the face, just a silhouette. Is the killer up there?

Choose:

- You could try to take Lord Carntsey outside to safety. To do this, turn to page 82.

- You could go up to the gallery and investigate the stranger, but this would leave Lord Carntsey unprotected while you're on the stairs. If you want to risk doing this, turn to page 80.

- You could stay put and hope that you can prevent a killing. If you're sure you want to stay, with all the risks involved, turn to page 83.

You go up to the gallery

So as not to lose time, you sprint out of the hall, through the entrance area and up the stairs to the right side of the gallery. You fling the door open, breathless and panting. Sitting on the bench is your boss. You expect a friendly greeting. Instead:

'You blithering idiot, you've left Lord Carntsey unprotected. Get back downstairs fast.'

Rush down into the hall again, then decide:

- Either to try to take Lord Carntsey outside to safety, by going to page 82.

- Or, if you think he's safer in the hall, to stay put, by turning to page 83.

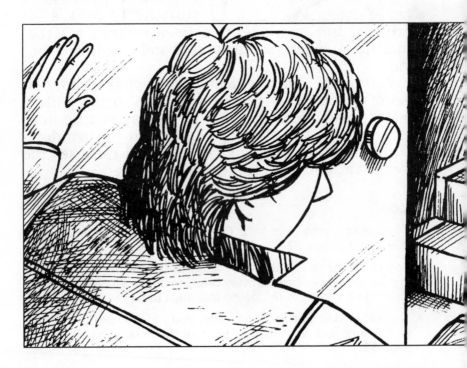

You try to take Lord Carntsey outside to safety

'I'm sorry. You must leave the hall at once,' you whisper to Lord Carntsey. 'It's simply too dangerous for you to remain here.' The music peters out as he stands up and turns towards the main doors.

'Don't go for a minute. I've already called the police and I've made everybody a nice cup of tea. We're much safer in here till they arrive.' It's Fred.

The parked bus you've seen crosses your mind. Could it represent danger outside the building just as great as any danger inside? The bus driver could be an assistant of the killer, waiting there just in case Lord Carntsey leaves the hall alive. The bus could be a get-away vehicle. You might well be safer inside. The arrival of the tea delays you, so you stay in the hall for now.

Go to page 83.

You stay put

Fred serves cups of tea from a tray and keeps telling everyone he's called the police as a security measure, presumably to keep them calm. As he does so, John is opening his instrument case as if to put his trombone back into it. Eric is fidgeting with one of his drums. He has the drumskin off and his hand is inside the base. Janet is holding what looks like a perfectly ordinary comb in her hand. Joyce, whose trumpet case you assume is still in the storeroom, is resting her trumpet on her knee. It is pointing at Lord Carntsey.

Your instinct tells you that an attempt at murder is going to happen in the next few seconds. Has your deduction and detection told you enough to prevent it?

You can't delay any longer. Right or wrong, you must make an arrest now. You must plunge forward to stop the person you think is the killer from committing murder in front of you. At least if you arrest the wrong person, the commotion might just stop the murder.

Decide who to arrest then write down your solution to the case. Remember, you need to get right:

• the name of the killer,

• the motive or reason for the assassination attempt,

• the method the killer is planning to use.

Finally, go to the mirror on page 84 to check your answer.

The Solution

Remember Mr Ditto? He was working for Special Branch, just as he told you on his visit to the Quicksolve office. So was Ms Noname and so was Tom the caretaker. He was not the real caretaker but an agent. He had been put into the hall to keep an eye on what was going on and to try to spot the killer. That's why he was killed, because he did spot the murderer getting ready to kill Lord Carntsey.

Remember the interview and written test answers given by the four musicians? They were very hard to use to identify the imposter – because none of the players was an imposter. They were all the people they were supposed to be and they all gave genuine answers to your questions to the best of their ability. They hadn't met each other before.

The real band conductor wasn't there, though no-one at the rehearsal knew that. He had been kidnapped by the killer and locked up for the day in the flat that rented as a base for the plot. He was lucky not to be killed, although Mr Ditto and Tom were murdered only because they would have revealed the killer's identity.

Ditto gave the real clue when he talked about what sounded like 'school dinner.' (Did you read page 29?) He was trying to name Schudanner. Fred Schudanner intended to tell everyone that the real conductor was off ill and that he, Schudanner, was the replacement. His plan was to kill Lord Carntsey at the performance, not from the platform at all, but by poisoning the coffee he would drink at the interval. When you turned up and told Schudanner you were from Quicksolve, he guessed that Tom was also watching him. So he decided that he had to act fast and kill Lord Carntsey when he arrived to meet the replacement players, instead of at the performance.

84

He made one slip when he 'found' the gun that he himself had placed in the trumpet case to try to incriminate Joyce Crabtree: he identified it as an M10. The M10 is a weapon popular with terrorists, but a Salvation Army band conductor would have been extremely unlikely to be able to recognize and identify one. Schudanner knew it was a quiet weapon, even indoors. That is why he knew he could get away with shooting Tom. With closed doors between the storeroom and the hall no-one heard the shot. He had brought the gun in case he had to shoot his way out of the hall.

His motive for killing Lord Carntsey was money, because he was simply being paid for a contract job. The man who hired him was the other Tom, Tom Davies, the general manager of Lord Carntsey's factories. With Lord Carntsey dead, Tom Davies would inherit the Carntsey Patent and was going to sell it to the highest bidder. Schudanner didn't even need to know what the priceless Patent was. It would simply have gone to Tom Davies by proper legal process when Lord Carntsey's will was put into action.

The method the killer was about to use to murder Lord Carntsey was poison. He was serving tea to everyone from cups on a tray, not pouring from a pot. He'd put enough poison in Lord Carntsey's cup to kill him ten times over. By the time Lord Carntsey had started to be ill, which would not have been for some minutes, Schudanner would have left the building to make his escape. He could have used the excuse of looking out for the arrival of the police, whom he'd never really sent for as he claimed.

So the killer was Schudanner, the motive (reason) for the assassination attempt was money, or you can count the Patent, and the method was poison. These are the three parts of the solution to the case. What about those suspicious parked buses on page 31 and

85

69? They were ordinary buses staffed by real bus drivers. Red herrings!

Go to page 87 to work out your final score.

Working Out Your Final Score

Since the morning, you have spent 6 hours working on the case **plus** the extra hours you chose to clock up or found you had to spend as the case went along.

First, calculate your total time score by adding 6 hours to the number of (extra) hours you have already noted down during the investigation. The maximum number of extra hours you may have spent is 8 hours and the minimum is 3 hours, because you couldn't avoid passing through two sections that made you add to your time score. So your total time score will be between 9 and 14 hours.

Next, give yourself **1 penalty point** for each hour in your total time score.

Now add **10 penalty points** for each of the three parts of the solution you got **wrong**: the **killer**, the **motive** or reason for the crime and the **method** the killer intended to use. Do not add anything for parts you got right.

Your final score is your total number of penalty points. The lower it is, the better. In fact the minimum score is 9 penalty points.

- If you scored 11 penalty points or less, go to page 89.

- If you scored 12 penalty points or more, go to page 88.

Time Score

~~1 hour~~ ~~2 hours~~ ~~3 hours~~ ~~4 hours~~ 5 hours

5 + 6 = 11 hours = 11 penalty points

Solution

Killer, motive right = no penalty points

Method wrong = 10 penalty points

Final Score

11 + 10 = 21 penalty points

If you scored 12 penalty points or more

'Well, I expect to hear a little less from you about how indispensable you are to the firm,' says the Boss, cheerlessly, as soon as you've got back to the office. 'Without me in the gallery at the finish to pick up the pieces we'd have been right down the plug-hole on that case!'

'Um, er,' you mumble.

'I think for the moment the best thing you can do is to detect a good pub and take me out for lunch to take my mind off your performance,' says the Boss, pushing the point home.

'Sorry, I can't do that,' you answer.

'Why not?'

'Salvationists don't drink alcohol – I've learned something on this case – but I'll buy you a nice glass of mineral water instead.' You duck as the telephone directory comes flying past your head.

THE END

If you scored 11 penalty points or less

'Well,' says Ms Noname, 'did you enjoy the concert?'

'Super,' you answer, 'and Lord Carntsey raised his thousands for the Salvation Army. Thank you for that fantastic meal afterwards,' you add, 'after all it was on your Special Branch department budget.'

'We don't have six-course meals every day,' she laughs.

'Look, you're not really called Noname are you? Call me ...,' you tell her your first name.

'No, Noname's not my real name,' she says, 'I'm called Gloria Nemo.'

'Well, thanks for your help, Gloria. It all worked out in the end.'

'Can I give you a lift home?'

'Yes – er, no thanks.' You remember her terrifying driving. 'I'll take a taxi.' From the depths of her handbag a mobile phone is beeping. She takes it out and answers it:

'Yes ... of course you can have a word.' She hands you the phone. 'Your boss.'

You decide that this is the time to make your escape. Giving her a wave of goodbye and mouthing to her to tell the Boss you're not there, you run off down the street, out of this story into the next.

THE END

Notes for Teachers

Blood and Fire can be used as a class library book in Key Stage 2 or to stretch able youngsters in this stage in RE. It can be used as part of the RE programme in Key Stage 3 or for lower-ability youngsters in Key Stage 4. It provides an opportunity to learn about Christian worship, beliefs and practice, and an opportunity to develop skills in evaluating evidence. It is intended to complement two earlier books in the series – *Sudden Death at the Vicarage*, which was in an Anglican setting, and *The Missing Minister*, which was in a Baptist setting – this time by providing a Salvation Army setting (see SCAA Model Syllabus 1, 1994 Christianity 3a, pages 42–43).

Both National RE Model Syllabuses have as attainment targets 'Learning about Religions' and 'Learning from Religion' (*ibid*. page 7) and list as appropriate skills and processes: investigation, interpretation, reflection, empathy, evaluation, analysis, synthesis, application and expression. Most of these are addressed in this book, some in depth, e.g. evaluation and analysis. Where the book is being used in group work it will also encourage the identified attitudes (*ibid*. page 8) of fairness, respect and enquiry. Both National Model Syllabuses emphasize the distinctiveness of religions and by treating religions separately, the books in this series emphasize the uniqueness of each religion, so that pupils might start to acquire 'a coherent understanding of individual religions' (*ibid*. page 6). But it is only a start.

The '*3rd Perspective*' model syllabus (1994) also includes in its Key Stage 3 Christian Studies section: sin and salvation, experience as a way to truth, positive Christian action in ethical dilemmas, denominations and Christian exemplars. Material in this book addresses all these issues.

Cross-curricular skills – careful reading, analysis of data and decision-making – are all required throughout the text, and although there are choices and decisions for readers to make, the text is looped in such a way that all readers will read most of the text at some point in their progress through the book.

In particular *Blood and Fire* can be used:

• to introduce Christianity in an unexpected way in Key Stage 3, dissolving some pupil expectations that RE is a predictably routine subject

- before interviewing a Salvationist officer, young soldier, songster, etc., as part of a unit on Christianity in RE, so that the experience of the interviewee can be compared with roles within the story

- to introduce or revise a class visit in Christian Studies in a highly unusual way – in the text everyone visits the citadel as part of the detective trail

- to lead to an imaginative approach to studying places of worship and not merely a historical approach, providing an affective rather than a merely factual angle to learning in RE

- as an opportunity in Key Stage 3 for pairs or groups of youngsters to work together, negotiating paths to follow and discussing options as they progress through the case, and developing group-work skills in the process

- as a thriller for when the teacher is absent, to prevent classes from terrorizing the supply teacher!

- as an absorbing homework task which youngsters will want to finish to see 'whodunnit'. Experience with earlier books in the series suggests that youngsters will go back after reaching the end to read the clues they've missed

- to address content identified in both National Model Syllabuses on the nature of the church or similar content in local agreed syllabuses for RE

- above all, to show that **RE can be fun!**

Using the genre of the mystery detective story, and a Salvationist setting, the reader is introduced to various concept and content areas in RE:

- Salvationist symbols: the badge, the flag, the mercy seat, the uniform, the military language

- Salvationist personnel: officers, soldiers, young soldiers, songsters, attenders

- Salvationist beliefs, including what the Articles of War are and basic Salvationist organization

- Salvationist social involvement globally and in the UK and the motivation for this work

- the activities of a Christian community and the reasons for commitment of some of its members (a local Salvationist corps)
- aspects of William Booth's life and work
- how people may come to be Salvationists (based on real-life cases)

This book is **not** intended to replace systematic, careful study of Christianity or of churches or the Salvation Army. While the writer has tried to avoid stereotyping, in a RE lesson youngsters may need to be cautioned to avoid making generalizations. Clearly not all Christians or Salvationist Christians would think, talk or behave as the ones in this **story** do.

Salvation Army resources

The Salvation Army Territorial Headquarters Communications Resource Department, at 101 Queen Victoria Street, London EC4P 4EP, provides a list of purchaseable resources suitable for further reading, school use or teacher preparation.

A final note of caution to the teacher

One teacher told me that she wondered why, while working on an earlier book in the series, so many youngsters kept asking if they could go to the toilet. Had suspense, as is so often the case in real life, produced a full bladder? It was some time before she realized that toilets have mirrors and they were trying to cheat on the solution by taking the book with them. Be warned!